THE BEST OF

1998

MATTHEW PRITCHETT studied at St Martin's School of Art in London and first saw himself published in the *New Statesman* during one of its rare lapses from high seriousness. He has been *The Daily Telegraph's* front-page pocket cartoonist since 1988. In 1995 and 1996 he was the winner of the Cartoon Arts Trust Award, in 1991 he was 'What the Papers Say' Cartoonist of the Year and in 1996 and 1998 he was *UK Press Gazette* Cartoonist of the Year.

The Daily Telegraph

THE BEST OF

MATT

1998

'When I was your age we had
to make our own accidents'

ORION

Orion Books
A Division of the Orion Publishing Group Ltd
Orion House
5 Upper St Martin's Lane
London WC2H 9EA

First published by Orion Books 1998

The right of Matthew Pritchett to be identified as the
author of this work has been asserted by him in accordance
with the Copyright, Designs and Patents Act, 1988

A CIP catalogue record for this book is available
from the British Library

ISBN 0 75281 723 X

Printed and bound in Great Britain by
The Guernsey Press Co. Ltd, Guernsey, Channel Islands

THE BEST OF

'OUCH'

Sporting Gestures

'Pepper, signor?'

Footballing gaffes as England play Italy

Sporting Gestures

World Cup ticket shortage hits UK fans

Sporting Gestures

'Sacré bleu! It's impossible to get tickets for the Eurovision Song Contest in Birmingham'

Sporting Gestures

'I drank so much last night that I can't even remember if I'm in the England World Cup squad'

Players dropped after late night drinking sessions break team fitness rules

Sporting Gestures

Hooligan fans hit France

Sporting Gestures

Scotland out, England in trouble

Sporting Gestures

'I was kept up all night
by my parents crying
over the football'

The end is in sight

Sporting Gestures

'Right, we should just make it
to Wimbledon before the
English are knocked out'

England knocked out, and it's not just
the football

Sporting Gestures

MCC says no to the ladies – again, as
Boycott moves house

Town and Country

Countryside march brings thousands to London

Town and Country

'You don't understand London ways. They have to be controlled and it's all over very quickly'

'I see you've picked up those smart London ways'

Town and Country

WINNER OF THE 1998 MOST ANGRY VILLAGE AWARD

'Is this supper or a Countryside Protest?'

Town and Country

'Two for lunch please'

'We've named this rose
the NHS Waiting List'

Annual Chelsea Flower Show brings
in the crowds

Foreign Affairs

'On a clear day, President Chirac, you can see the lorries stuck at Calais'

French lorry drivers blockade roads and ports

'Dad, I'm going backpacking through India and Pakistan'

India and Pakistan indulge in tit-for-tat nuclear testing

Foreign Affairs

'Now it's turning really
nasty - they're planting
Leylandii trees along the border'

Foreign Affairs

'Does it say when the military action against Iraq will start?'

US plans direct action on Iraq's chemical weapons

Foreign Affairs

'I want to go abroad but I'm worried that Robin Cook has given the British a bad name'

'I'm not sure I'd want to buy weapons from a man like Robin Cook'

Foreign Office chief Cook in trouble

Foreign Affairs

'In the Foreign Office it's
not who you know, it's what
you don't know'

'You mean we're an arms
supplier? Why wasn't I told?'

Foreign Affairs

President Clinton has girl(s) trouble

The Nation's Health

'I'm afraid I'm going to have to take a sample of cash from you'

'We're going to try to remove the bit about shorter waiting lists'

New Labour struggles to keep its pre-election promises

The Nation's Health

'It's yours if you take your
name off the waiting list'

'We're so busy that I never
see my wife – and now she's
left me for an older man'

NHS still fighting waiting lists as new impotence
drug discovered

The Nation's Health

'Well, that's used up
the extra cash for the NHS'

'You mean you called me out in
the middle of the night to wish
the NHS a happy 50th birthday?'

NHS gets small cash boost for its birthday

The Nation's Health

New report headlines danger for non-smokers

Our Nanny State

'Please can you help me work the video machine?'

'Dad, I advise you to do a runner'

Modern parenting according to New Labour

Our Nanny State

'If you're going to perform embarrassing U-turns, would you do it outside, please?'

'It's worth a try'

Government does U-turn on tobacco sponsorship as beef on the bone is banned

Our Nanny State

'Hurry up, come and eat your supper before the government decides to ban it'

Our Nanny State

Our Nanny State

'We discovered Bovine Spongiform Encephalopathy in 1985, but it was two years before any of us could pronounce it'

'It's not BSE. I'm afraid you've got the millennium bug'

The Political Picture

Conservatives change their image in wake of election defeat

The Political Picture

'Mmm, try that one, it's
compassionate with a hard edge'

'Oh no! I'm going
to have a job!'

Minister urged to 'think the unthinkable' on the
welfare state

The Political Picture

'Aaaarrgh! Look
it's Blackpool'

'Think the unthinkable —
get a job'

...And drop their old comforts

The Political Picture

Cash for access causes lobbying scandal

The Political Picture

The Orangemen's marching season begins as walkers fight for their rights

The Political Picture

'What?............EVERY hour?'

'Miss Swann, you don't look a day over 18 – which is why I'm going to pay you only £3 an hour'

Proposed minimum wage causes heartache on all sides

The Political Picture

'Sometimes I worry that being an MP is just a phase I'm going through'

'Son, there's something I have to tell you — I'm a hereditary peer'

Age of consent debate clashes with House of Lords reform

The Political Picture

'Our son is a bit of a hot headed political activist — he voted in the local elections'

Local elections make little impact

The Political Picture

Global markets crisis hits the City

The Political Picture

'So, what are we going to do about the strong pound?'

'How much does Sir want to spend? They range from prudent to gigantic economic miscalculation'

The Political Picture

'Oh look, a note
from Alastair Campbell'

'It's obviously just a
fuss about nothing'

This cartoon was vetted by P. Mandelson

The spin doctors get tough...

The Political Picture

'Tony Blair is coming on the programme to deny that he only does soft interviews'

'Well, I want him to see my medals'

...As old soldiers demand apology from Japanese Emperor

The Political Picture

New Labour means Cool Britannia

The Political Picture

'I hate Tuesdays, it's
double Heroin followed by
Cocaine Studies'

'WOW, fantastic,
pass this round'

The Government puts drugs on
everyone's agenda

A British Obsession

'I'd like to change this for
one that says Sea View'

'You're cleared for
landing, Selsey'

At the turn of the year a surprise tornado lifted a
town from its foundations

A British Obsession

'This is nothing; in Britain we've had floods, sleet, storms...'

'Wimbledon? Follow that cloud'

Bizarre spring conditions as Briton reaches North Pole give way to summer deluge

A British Obsession

'The good news is we get a winter heating payment – the bad news is we've spent it this July'

Travelling Light

Fire in fast food joint hits air travellers

Travelling Light

'I don't know much about art, but I know a near miss when I see one'

'Welcome aboard Concorde, most of the plane will be flying at 51,000 feet'

British Airways invest in snazzy new corporate logo as Concorde hits trouble

Travelling Light

'Ha, ha, ha! It will be a slow and lingering death'

'The train left ten minutes ago – if you run you can catch it'

High speed rail link hits the buffers again

Travelling Light

'I'm so terribly sorry, but from the back you looked like John Prescott'

'I'm just going for one last drive in the car before the Budget'

New Labour promotes public transport by hitting the driver's pocket

Travelling Light

'I'm a motorist, I've paid already'

Travelling Light

'Either we've gone through the sound barrier, or our exhaust has just fallen off again'

New land speed record set in USA

The Devolution Debate

'Future generations will take the Welsh assembly for granted, but we're the ones who nearly bothered to vote for it'

'I see it as a moral victory for the Don't Knows'

The Welsh are underwhelmed by the opportunity for independence

The Devolution Debate

'Are you Jones-the-Yes
or Jones-the-No?'

'I once saw a blurred photo
of a Scotsman who was
willing to pay more tax, but
I think it was a hoax'

As the Scots are made to pay for it

The Devolution Debate

'Your mother and I would like to give you the chance to break away and start raising your own revenue'

'My accountant says we should run away to England'

We're Domed

'I'm resigning, the whole thing is a fiasco'

'Put it this way – if your body was on show in the Dome I wouldn't want to walk through it'

The Millennium Dome causes controversy...

We're Domed

'And I hope we'll be seeing you in the Millennium Dome'

'Mummy, is the minister without portfolio everywhere?'

...As the Church gets in on the act

Nuclear Nonsense

UK accepts foreign nuclear waste...

Nuclear Nonsense

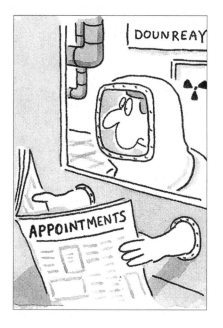 

...As Dounreay is scheduled for shutdown

The Best Years of Your Life

'If the Chancellor says having a family is such a good idea, why hasn't he got one?'

'Dad, can I borrow the go-kart?'

Government promotes 'the family' but criticises teenage couples

The Best Years of Your Life

'Your university days are some
of the happiest of my life'

'I took a week off sick and,
blow me, I fell ill!'

Students pay to learn while millions are lost to
industry

Law and Order

'In mitigation, M' lud, my client's crime was not considered serious enough to warrant serialisation'

. . . "By the way," said Ted, "I really love China."
"Yes, and it's got great leaders, too," replied Frank . . .

Media up in arms over payments to criminals and censorship of Chris Patten's memoirs

Law and Order

'Please don't send me to the Maze — I've got no experience of running a prison'

Prisoners running jails as others risk jail for their right of way

Law and Order

'It came out in court that the £2m I stole from the bank belonged to my defence lawyer'

BODY PARTS SCULPTOR GUILTY

'I'm pleased to say this case has cost an arm and a leg'

Legal fat cats in the money again

Law and Order

'We know you're in there,
Chief Constable, come out
with your P45'

'My goodness, Rex, I had
no idea you were a Mason'

Police held to account for blunders and
undeclared interests

Public and Private

'I hope that's a plane and not our share price'

Is It Art?

'LOOK OUT !
Ice lollies straight ahead!'

'There aren't enough Oscars for
everyone − lock the 3rd class
guests down below'

TITANIC! The biggest disaster movie ever

Is It Art?

From Aliens to Animal Crackers

'Yes, sir, the bottled water was £300,000,000 because it came from the moon'

Evidence of water found on the moon...

From Aliens to Animal Crackers

...As science fiction looks like becoming a reality

From Aliens to Animal Crackers

'I suppose that means
I'll have to redecorate
the sitting room after all'

From Aliens to Animal Crackers

'I'd like to offer a home for eight rashers of streaky bacon'

Two Tamworth Red pigs go on the run from slaughterhouse

And Finally...

'Fifty years ago I invited him in to watch the Royal wedding on television . . .'

'I'm going to have one final bath with Britannia'

The Royals celebrate an anniversary and lose an old friend

And Finally...